Purpose of:
The Little People's Guide To the Big World— Parent/Child Edition

A word to Parents, Teachers and Children:

Growing up today can be like walking through a mine field. Children are faced with disturbing obstacles like peer pressure, substance abuse, broken homes and a host of potential disasters. "Prevention is paramount," says Trevor Romain, author of this book. "Children who know about a problem in advance can deal with situations better than children taken by surprise."

Concerned Businesses, Professional Leaders and Industry's Response:

The Little People's Guide To The Big World—Parent/Child Edition is a collection of poems which help clarify the difficult issues children deal with in today's world. Parents can't be there with their children every minute, but children can open up this book anytime for some down to earth friendly information presented in a bright and entertaining format. We know you welcome the action of concerned business and professional people who are acting to make a difference in children's lives. This gift is their way of saying, "We care and want to help." Teachers and parents can encourage the continuance of this program by expressing their appreciation to those responsible for this gift.

We trust that *The Little People's Guide To The Big World—Par* *Edition* will become one of your family's favorite books.

The Pub

D1376874

Praise For *The Little People's Guide To The Big World—Parent/Child Edition*

"The reader-friendly book belongs in every household, the best reference book a child could hope for." **Blair Corning, San Antonio Express News**

"I am most impressed with the way in which the book is intended to be used--parents teaching children--an open relationship where emotions can be easily expressed." **Kimberly Copeland, M.A., Licensed Professional Counselor, Lubbock, Texas**

"This book speaks to children at their level about many subjects, of which adults are often lost for words." **Bruce Erley, V.P. Marketing, Up With People, Broomfield, Colorado**

The Little People's Guide To The Big World—Parent/Child Edition is dedicated to children everywhere whose health and well being are the primary focus of businesses, professional people and industry across the country.

This book has been produced for children and their parents as a means of reference for everyday events that may occur in the child's life.

Poems and Illustrations provided by T.Romain & J.Dalpiaz

Eleventh Edition 2017

Published and distributed exclusively by:

Family Concepts, Ltd.

P. O. Box 551236

Gastonia, NC 28055

Telephone 704-824-2859

Copyright© 1996 by Trevor Romain

Printed in China

All rights reserved. No part of this book may be reproduced or transmitted in any form or by any means, electronic or mechanical, including photocopying, or by any information storage and retrieval system, without permission in writing from the publisher.

The businesses listed on page 5 wish to provide you and your child with this Child I.D. and Information page.

Personal Information

Name _____

Address_____

City_____ State____ Zip_____

Height _____ Weight _____ Race _____

Hair Color_____ Eye Color_____ Sex_____

Birthdate_____ Blood Type_____

Parent Name_____ Phone _____

Parent Name_____ Phone _____

Emergency:

Contact _____ Phone _____

Information For Babysitter

Dr.'s Name _____

Dentist's Name _____

Nearest Relative _____ Phone _____

My Picture

Fingerprints

L. Little	L. Ring	L. Middle	L. Index	L. Thumb	R. Thumb	R. Index	R. Middle	R. Ring	R. Little

Contents

*"When you read, you go on great adventures!
Read and experience the world!
With this in mind, we are pleased to provide this special gift
to you and other avid readers in the making."*

tropicalCAFE
SMOOTHIE
eat better. feel better.

VENTURE RVG
REALTY GROUP

High Hopes
Veterinary Care
102 Rainbow Dr. • 501-941-2273

PERSONAL TOUCH
Impressions
EMBROIDERY SCREEN PRINT CAD-CUT GRAPHIC DESIGN
918 W. Main Street • 501-941-1662

CABOT
OFFICE MACHINES, INC

P★GE
& company
DanceAcademy

Greystone Rx
Community Pharmacy

the
FURNITURE
Store
• Downtown Cabot •
501.843.4221
Shop Us First and You Will... Shop us Last!

READING

If you want to be smart. Read.

If you want to do well at school. Read.

If you want to be different. Read.

If you want to know everything. Read.

If you want to be the best. Read.

If you want to be better than the best. Read.

But if you want to walk around your whole life saying, "Huh?" Then don't read.

TRYING HARDER

Sometimes it seems
the harder you try
the harder it is
to try and get by.

But just when you think
you can't try anymore
when you want to give up
and crawl on the floor:

Stop for a second
and look deep inside
you'll find a spark
a spark we call pride.

Then try again
with all your might
reach for your goal
and keep it in sight.

Never give up
never give in
if you try real hard
I promise you'll win.

GOING TO THE HOSPITAL

Rest in the hospital
is good for you
when you get out
you'll be good as new.

Hospitals help
the sick to get well
the nurses are nice
and the doctors are swell.

If you have to go
don't feel sad
it's not that scary
and not that bad.

Once you get better
and your illness is cured
you'll leave there quick
yes, rest assured.

TAKING CARE OF YOUR PETS

Feed your pets well
and keep them clean
always give them water
and never be mean.

Visit the veterinarian
for a regular check-up
and always pay attention
to your kitten or pup.

Look after your pet
and give it love
no matter if it's a gerbil
or a lizard or a dove.

MANNERS

Be polite
and respect the old
listen to teachers
and do what you're told.

Don't interrupt
when people are speaking
if something is private
there shouldn't be peeking.

Cover your mouth
when you're going to yawn.
Cough and sneeze
in the crook of your arm.

Try not to talk
with a mouth full of food
be well behaved
and don't be rude.

Don't burp, don't spit
and don't pick your nose
be true to your friends
and don't step on their toes.

11

MOVING

Moving is fun
moving is sad
it can make you feel good
it can make you feel bad.

It's tough to leave
your friends behind
and you're never quite sure
what you're going to find.

What's great about moving
is seeing new places
meeting new friends
and exploring new spaces.

It's so hard to be
the new kid on the block
but it doesn't take long
to get over the shock.

You can write old friends
and phone them too
discuss what's happening
tell them what's new.

Before you know it
you'll be safe and sound
enjoying the bunch
of new friends around.

GLASSES

There are people with glasses
all over the place
just like your hair
they become part of your face.

It won't take too long
to forget they are there
and people won't see them
they won't even stare.

You'll feel a lot better
your eyes will too
you'll see more clearly
with a better view.

So, if you don't see well
or maybe see a hazy mist
the person who can help
is called an optometrist.

TALKING TO PEOPLE WHO CARE

If *you* feel bad
or unhappy inside
and need to discuss
the feelings you hide,

Talk to your family
or talk to a friend
don't keep it in
until the end.

Talking helps
to bring things out
things that frustrate you
and make you shout.

Talking is great
it opens your mind
it often solves problems
and helps you unwind.

There are people who care
who are waiting for you
to help you with problems
and make dreams come true.

DEALING WITH DEATH

When someone you love
suddenly dies
everyone hurts
and everyone cries.

It helps to talk
to your mom or dad
about the person
and the life they had.

Sometimes it's better
things happen that way
for those who are sick
and in pain every day.

It's not your fault
if someone is dead
don't let that thought
enter your head.

Death is sad
for grown-ups too
it doesn't seem fair
and hurts through and through.

It can make you angry
it can make you reel
but the more time passes
the better you'll feel.

When you think of that person
say a small prayer
and know that the memory
will always be there.

SERVING IN THE MILITARY

My daddy is in the military
and I'm not sure what he does
only that he helps other people
who need him very much.

My daddy is a soldier
he is often gone away
and we are so proud of him
in each and every way.

I really miss my daddy
when he doesn't come home
and I remember to say my prayers
so that daddy never feels alone.

Come home daddy
when your job is done
I know that those people need you
but they aren't the only ones.

TEAMWORK

A   team

        isn't   a   team

                        unless

                                  everyone   pulls   together

and   works   as   a   team.

Then everything clicks
just like a dream
and the team starts to work
like a machine.

Goals are reached
and games are won
members feel great
and jobs get done.

That's teamwork!

17

FIRE

If you're at home
and a fire breaks out
let everyone know
by giving a shout.

Walk, don't run
in case you might fall
and once you're out
give the firemen a call.

If the room fills with smoke
and you're still indoors
get close to the floor
and crawl on all fours.

The reason to crawl
is not a joke
it's just easier to breathe
under the smoke.

If your clothes are on fire
don't delay
roll on the floor
until the fire goes away.

Don't stop for a thing
not a pet, not a pan
just get out of the house
as quick as you can.

Don't fight the fire
it's stronger than you
just make sure that you're safe
that's the best thing to do.

HELPING OUT

We all do chores
it's part of life
for son and daughter
husband and wife.

Cleaning up
is always a pain
you have to do it
and do it again.

To make helping easy
call it a game
make up some rules
and give it a name.

Dirt and bugs
are bad for you
keep your room clean
that's what you should do.

Help your folks
try to be neat
when on clean floors
do have clean feet.

Do your chores
and do them well
and just by chance
your allowance might swell.

VISITING THE DOCTOR

Your doctor knows
exactly what to do
if you feel sick
or miserable or blue.

Doctors help
the sick to get well
they're always nice
and the nurses are swell.

If you have to go
don't feel sad
it's not that scary
and not that bad.

FRUITS AND VEGETABLES

Eat more fruits and vegetables
they are important for your health
the vitamins, minerals and fiber you get
are more important than wealth.

Fresh fruits and vegetables
help prevent disease
they come in a wide range of colors
that are natural and please.

Remember that fruits and vegetables
help keep us going
if you want a healthy life
it starts with knowing.

SAYING GOOD-BYE TO A FRIEND

Sometimes friends
have to move away
although you wish
so much they could stay.

There's nothing worse
than saying good-bye
it makes you sad
it makes you cry.

But listen up
there's something good
you'll have an *old* friend
in a *new* neighborhood.

You can visit
you can call
no need to worry
no need at all.

Because friends stay friends
through thick and thin
no matter what they do
no matter where they've been.

GETTING LOST

Getting lost
is not much fun
where should you go
where should you run?

The best thing to do
is stay where you are
your parents will find
you
if you don't go too far.

If you're in a store
or a big shopping mall
ask a cashier
to give them a call.

A uniformed guard
can help you out too
he's well trained
and knows what to do.

Don't be too scared
don't get a fright
you'll feel a lot better
with your parents in sight.

When next you go out
decide where to wait
in case you get lost
or someone is late.

ADOPTION

It's cool to be adopted
it happens all the time
becoming part of a new family
is really very fine.

Adoption happens
for one reason or another
and many times it can lead
to a new sister or brother.

A new family is formed
that has lots to give and share
and making you a special part of them
is a love beyond compare.

THE DENTIST

Visiting the dentist
is a good thing to do
he looks after your smile
and the way you chew.

Brush your teeth
and floss a lot
it will keep your teeth healthy
so they will not rot.

RECYCLING

Look all around you
so much paper and plastic
let us recycle
it is fantastic!

Do not forget about
all the cardboard and glass
you can recycle together
with your entire class.

It is up to good people
like you and me
to help save the planet
and set the world free.

Take care of your space
recycle and save
keep your eyes open
help others behave.

ODE TO LAW ENFORCEMENT

Support the ones who wear the badge
the ones who walk the beat
protect and keep them safe
while they are on the street.

As they wait and as they watch
doing good for all
guide their minds and give them strength
for each and every call.

Ready to put their lives on the line
give them courage each day
let them know that we are with them
in each and every way.

Let us pray for the ones who wear the badge
protect them from harm
always keep them safe
and in your loving arms.

FRIENDS

Friends are great
and easy to get
the times you have together
you will never forget.

Don't treat your friends
in an ugly way
because if you lose them
you'll be sorry one day.

Friends are there
through thin and thick
and will always be
if you're well or sick.

Treat them right
and love them all
so your friendship will stand
and never fall.

CONCENTRATION

Sometimes it's hard
to concentrate
when you want to play
and you just can't wait.

Your mind seems to drift
and your thoughts fly away
no matter how hard
you wish they would stay.

If you find
this is happening to you
give some thought
to what you can do.

Ask your mom or dad
and your teacher too
and they'll find a way
to help you through.

It's very important
to let them know
because you need concentration
for your mind to grow.

BRACES

Visiting an orthodontist's office
is the right thing to do
the doctor straightens your teeth
and helps with your chew.

Braces are good
they help with your smile
many people have them
but just for a while.

When you wear braces
especially at school
your friends will tell you
they look very COOL.

When you're older
and the braces are gone
you'll be very happy
you once had them on.

STRANGERS

Strangers are people
whom you don't know
if they come too close
just get up and go

Don't talk to strangers
and don't take a ride
if they try to touch you
they're just being sly

Find someone you know
or run to a store
if your parents aren't home
try the neighbor next door

Don't walk alone
when you're out and about
and if someone approaches you
give a loud shout

Sometimes strangers
look fine and okay
whatever they offer
you just say, "No way".

Tell someone you trust
and tell them fast
remember the place
the stranger was last

Ask mom and dad
the best thing to do
if the stranger should suddenly
come up to you

Hey little girl, want some candy?

GETTING SICK

Getting sick
is not much fun
but it happens sometimes
to everyone.

It's not that great
to stay in bed
with a drippy nose
or a pain in your head.

You can't go out
you feel really blah
you take some medicine
and say aaahhh..

But time passes by
and soon you feel right
no sneezing by day
no coughing by night.

Get plenty of rest
and stay indoors
keep out of damp places
and off of cold floors.

Keep yourself busy
with a book or a game
and before you know it
you'll be better again.

HAVING A BIG HEAD

If something really great
happens to you
don't get a BIG head
whatever you do.

Having a LARGE head
can put a strain on your back.
It can make your brain wobble
and cause your ears to flap.

You'll find it hard to walk
with your oversized head
and if you turn at night
you could slip off your bed.

And if you brag a lot
your head will grow some more
it might just get so big
that you crash right through the floor.

So may I please suggest
for the safety of us all
that you act quite nice and humble
and keep your big head small.

PUNISHMENT

If you are punished
for something bad
you'll probably feel angry
and get really mad.

It's pretty normal
to feel that way
whenever you're grounded
and don't get to play.

But give it some thought
and ask yourself why
you planned something bad
then gave it a try.

Punishment can happen
a reminder for you
to think very carefully
about all that you do.

LOSS OF A PET

Sometimes a pet
will get old and die
it can make you lonely
you might even cry.

But that's part of nature
and all you can do
is remember the pleasure
the pet brought to you.

If your pet is a bird
or a fish or a mouse
you can bury the pet
behind your house.

Ask your parents
to give you a hand
then bury your pet
under some sand.

Mark the place
and say a small prayer
leaving a memory
that will always be there.

Here Lies Bubbles

LONELINESS

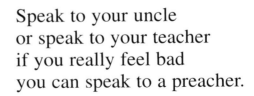

If you feel lonely
and empty inside
you just want to cry
or run out and hide,

Speak to your mom
or speak to your dad
and they'll find out
what's making you sad.

Speak to your uncle
or speak to your teacher
if you really feel bad
you can speak to a preacher.

But if no one's around
to help you out
do a puzzle
or even shout.

Think of things
that make you smile
read a book
or draw for a while.

Being by yourself
is sometimes fun
you can do it indoors
or in the sun.

Being alone
is not so bad
if you keep yourself busy
and happy and glad.

GETTING TO THE TOP

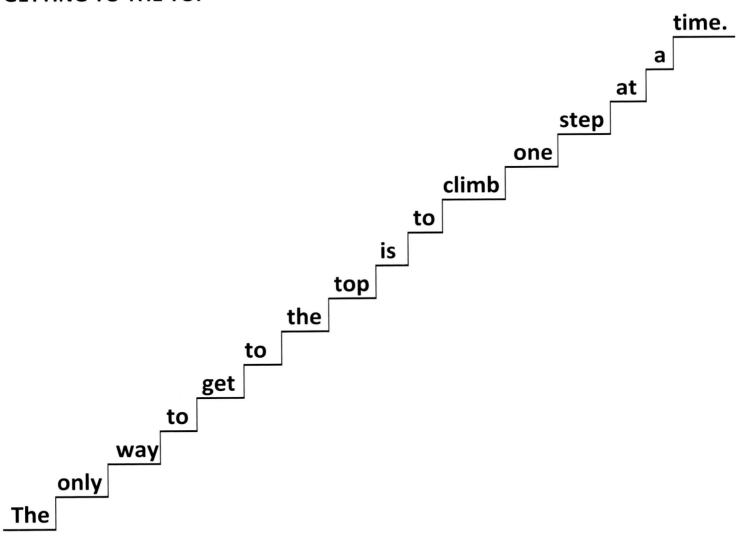

The only way to get to the top is to climb one step at a time.

SPORTSMANSHIP

(I wanted to scream and shout and tear up this page
because I just couldn't make it rhyme.
But, I'm a really good sport, so I left it exactly as it is.)

You should play hard and play fair but do not deliber-
ately break the rules to take advantage. People do not
like cheaters.

Never lose your temper and never ever fight. Fighting
will get you ejected from the game and suspended
from the team.

Do not make negative comments to the opposing team.
Winning is the best way to beat them. Nasty comments will not help you play any better.

Always thank the officials for their time and effort.
Without them you would not be able to enjoy the
game.

Shake hands with your opponents after the game and
thank them, even if you lose.

SAVING

Saving your money
is good for you
and opening an account
is easy to do.

The amount doesn't matter
no not at all
it may be big
and it may be small.

In an account
your money will grow
and in the end
you'll have more to show.

VISITING THE CHIROPRACTOR

If you want to be healthy, here's what to do.
Eat well, exercise and think good thoughts too.
Sleep every night so you get enough rest
And there's one more thing to help you be your best.

Did you ever hear that your brain runs the show?
So your body works right from your head to your toe.
When your brain is doing its job like it should
You'll heal when you're sick and you'll mostly feel good.

What doctor can help you to tune up your brain?
It's your family chiropractor, let me explain.
Your bones have to line up for you to be strong
And your chiropractor puts them back where they belong.

BABY-SITTERS

If your baby-sitter
does something wrong
and acts kind of strange
while your parents are
gone.

Like has weird friends
that come to your home
who drink and smoke
and sit on the phone.

Don't be afraid
don't be upset
but it's very important
that you don't forget.

To tell mom or dad
make sure that they know
what the sitter does
after they go.

SELFISH

Just to show you how a person can be selfish...
I am not going to do a drawing
or even write a poem on this page

BULLY TROUBLE

Bullies are mean
bullies don't care
they pull on your ears
then pull on your hair.

Bullies have problems
that make them real bad
sometimes they're lonely
or angry or sad.

Bullies enjoy
making you squirm
they want you to crawl
like a scared little worm.

Some bullies have gangs
that make them feel strong
If they head your way
you should move right along.

Then tell your parents
or a trusted grown up
and they'll make sure
the bully will stop.

Don't feel ashamed
about turning them in
It's the only way
you can ever win.

DRUGS

Drugs are awful
they play with your brain
they make you feel weird
they drive you insane.

If someone says
that drugs can't hurt
just think of the addicts
who live in the dirt.

Drugs steal your life
and mess with your soul
wearing you down
is their only goal.

Don't take a chance
just pass them by
even if good friends
beg you to try.

JEALOUSY

There's a certain feeling
that makes you feel bad
when someone has something
that you wish *you* had.

They call it being jealous
that feeling you get
it makes you irritable
it makes you fret.

Don't feel alone
it happens a lot
to all sorts of people
who want more than they've got.

But we can't always have
all that's in sight
if you enjoy what you've got
then you've seen the light.

HURT FEELINGS

Sometimes people
say things to you
that are mean and ugly
and often not true.

And what they say
makes you feel so bad
that you just want to cry
and get really mad.

The best thing to do
is pretend you don't care
that they hurt your feelings
and they are not fair.

Try to keep smiling
and don't show your pain
they'll soon get bored
and not hurt you again.

Often we say things
that hurt deep inside
and as soon as we say them
we wish we could hide.

So say what you mean
and mean what you say
and always think
before blabbering away.

EXERCISE

Exercise is easy
and so fun to do
just make up your mind
to feel good as new.

Some people will walk
while others take a hike
exercise may include swimming
jumping or riding a bike.

Moving is the key
to staying healthy and fit
and the opposite of exercise
is to do nothing and sit.

Let's all try hard
to have fun and go play
anyway we exercise our bodies
will promote a better day.

BEING DIFFERENT

As you grow up
you'll see new things
like horses that dance
or a dog that sings.

You'll also see kids
who are different from
you
some have one arm
or a back that's askew.

Others have braces
so they can walk
some have machines
to help them talk.

Some kids have cancer
and lose all their hair
it's really sad
and seems so unfair.

Please treat these people
like your friends treat
you
be nice and warm
be honest and true.

All that they want
is to be treated the same
not cast aside
or called a bad name.

Accept different people
try to be fair
hold out your hand
and show them you care.

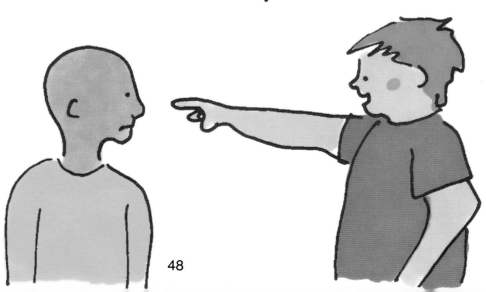

48

GUNS

A Gun is a weapon
it's not a toy
it should never be touched
by a girl or a boy

Guns are dangerous
unless you are trained
and even then
you could be maimed

Don't fool around
or mess with a gun
even if you are playing
and having fun

If you see a gun
keep away
and tell a grownup
it's not for play

NEVER FORGET

Never forget
when someone is nice
never forget
bruises need ice.

Never forget
who helped you to learn
never forget
that fire can burn.

Never forget
those who have died
never forget
the tears you have cried.

Never forget
tomorrow will come
never forget
the warmth of the sun.

Never forget
that bad words hurt
never forget
germs live in dirt.

Never forget
that a rainbow needs rain
and never forget
that being nasty brings pain.